DREAMLAND PUBLICATIONS

J-128, KIRTI NAGAR, NEW DELHI-110 015, INDIA

PHONE : +91-11-2510 6050, 2543 5657

E-mail : dreamland@vsnl.com

Shop online at www.dreamlandpublications.com

Like us on www.facebook.com/DreamlandPublications

Published in 2019 by
DREAMLAND PUBLICATIONS
J-128, Kirti Nagar, New Delhi - 110 015, India
Tel : +91-11-2510 6050, 2543 5657
E-mail : dreamland@vsnl.com, www.dreamlandpublications.com
Printed in India

Contents

1. THE TOWN MOUSE AND THE COUNTRY MOUSE

Once, the country mouse invited his friend, the town mouse, to visit him. The town mouse loved the fresh air of the countryside. But as they fed only on grains and some fruits, he began to miss the town life. He spoke of all the good food he ate, and invited the country mouse to go with him. The town mouse lived in a small but luxurious house. There was no garden; instead there was a large cupboard full of many fruits besides cheese, bread, and cakes! But both the mice had to hide in some hole, when a cat, woman, or child passed by. After a few days, the country mouse turned very pale. Bidding farewell, he told his friend: 'You have rich food and luxury, but I have much more peace than you.'

2. THE BLUE-DYED JACKAL

Long ago, a jackal that lived in a forest, entered a village washerman's house in search of food. He fell into a drum which had blue dye, and was stained blue all over! When he returned to the forest, all the animals stared at the strange creature. The jackal cunningly said: 'God has made me your king.' All the animals had to serve him, even the tigers and lions! To prevent recognition, the blue jackal drove the other jackals out of the forest. One day, as he was holding court, a passing pack of jackals began to howl. Unable to control himself, the blue jackal also started howling! Finding out the truth, the angry animals chased him out of the forest.

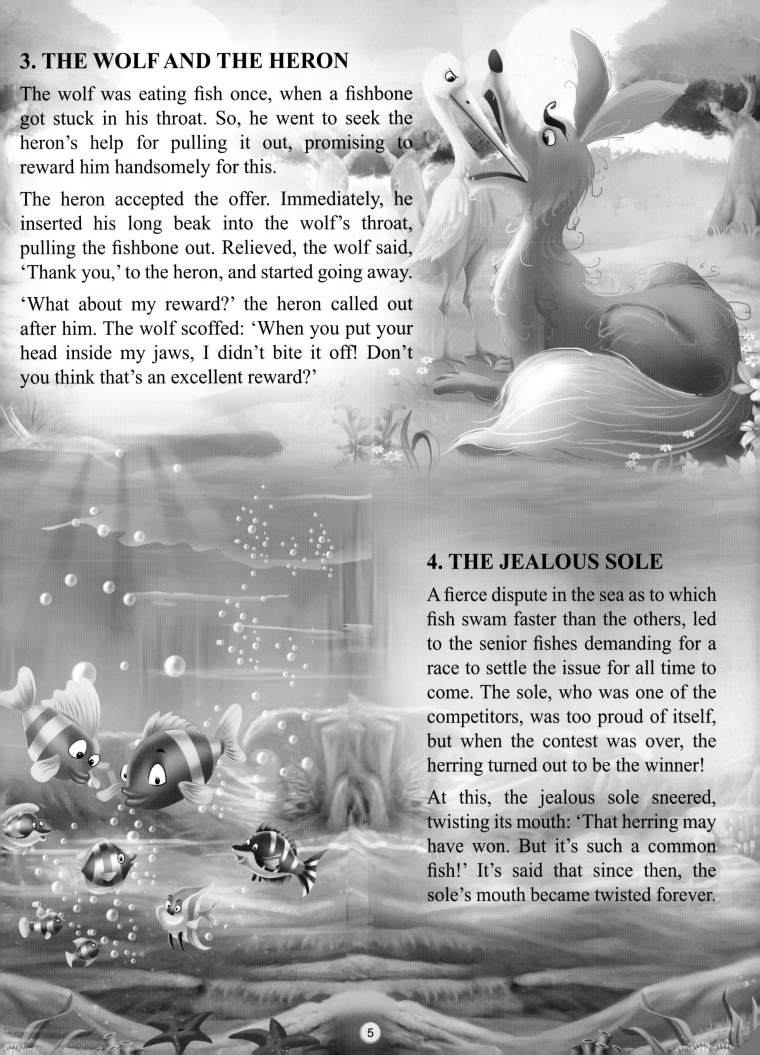

3. THE WOLF AND THE HERON

The wolf was eating fish once, when a fishbone got stuck in his throat. So, he went to seek the heron's help for pulling it out, promising to reward him handsomely for this.

The heron accepted the offer. Immediately, he inserted his long beak into the wolf's throat, pulling the fishbone out. Relieved, the wolf said, 'Thank you,' to the heron, and started going away.

'What about my reward?' the heron called out after him. The wolf scoffed: 'When you put your head inside my jaws, I didn't bite it off! Don't you think that's an excellent reward?'

4. THE JEALOUS SOLE

A fierce dispute in the sea as to which fish swam faster than the others, led to the senior fishes demanding for a race to settle the issue for all time to come. The sole, who was one of the competitors, was too proud of itself, but when the contest was over, the herring turned out to be the winner!

At this, the jealous sole sneered, twisting its mouth: 'That herring may have won. But it's such a common fish!' It's said that since then, the sole's mouth became twisted forever.

5. UNITY IS STRENGTH

Once upon a time, a flock of parrots lived on a huge banyan tree. One day, a bird catcher laid a net beneath the tree and spread some grains over it. Then he hid in a nearby bush. Some parrots saw the grains. Soon all the parrots were pecking at them. They did not see the hidden net, and got trapped in it! Desperately the parrots fluttered their wings to get out of it, but in vain.

The leader of the parrots was very intelligent. He said: 'My friends, let us unite and free ourselves.' The parrots listened to his plan, and did as he said. All of them flapped their wings hard and flew up in the sky with the net. The bird catcher looked up in astonishment. Though he tried, he couldn't catch them.

The flock flew for awhile before going to meet a mouse, who was their leader's friend. The mouse and his family nibbled at the net and freed the birds. The parrots thanked them, and flew away.

6. THE STORY OF TWO CATS

One day, two cats reached a king's palace in search of food. It so happened, that the day before, some cats had infested the king's palace and destroyed his beautiful garden. The angry king issued an order that any cat entering the palace, or seen around it, would be put to death instantly. As the two cats reached the palace gate, another cat who was fleeing, told them of the king's orders. But the greedy cats went inside. Leaping through a window, they pounced on a plate of fish inside the hall. A royal servant at once seized them and killed them.

7. THE ELEPHANTS AND THE KING OF MICE

Long ago, there lived a huge group of mice in a forest, which had a big lake. One day, an elephant herd came that way in search of water, and some mice got crushed under their heavy feet. The elephants started coming daily, and many mice got killed each day. So, the king of mice approached the elephant chief and requested him to guide his herd through another route. He promised to help the elephants one day in return. The elephant chief smiled at this, but agreed to take change his route. One day, a group of hunters came to the forest, and trapped the elephants in strong nets. The elephants struggled hard to free themselves, but all in vain. A mouse happened to pass by. He ran straight to his king, who immediately took the entire group of mice to rescue the elephants. The mice at once cut open the nets with their sharp teeth. The elephants were set free. They were very grateful to the mice for their great help and became friends forever.

8. THE TRUTHFUL DEER

Once, amidst a dense forest, a hunter had perched himself atop a tree as he waited for game. He spotted a deer far off. Just as he was about to take aim, the deer ran up to the surprised hunter and said: 'My wife and children are waiting for me at home. Please let me go. I promise I will come back, after leaving them in someone's care.'

The hunter let the deer go. When the deer met his family, his children were happy to see him. But when he told them what had happened, they too decided to go with him. When the deer reached the hunter with his family, he said: 'I have kept my promise. Now you may kill us.' The hunter was moved by the love of the deer family and the deer's honesty. Gazing at the deer, he said, 'If I were to kill you, God would never forgive me.' So saying, the hunter freed the deer and his family. He also broke his bow, and vowed to give up killing innocent animals.

9. THE LION AND THE BEAR

A long time ago, a lion and a bear killed a deer at the same moment. They did not want to share the prey and began to fight over it. They fought so furiously that they got very tired, and had to lie down. A fox had been watching them from a distance.

The cunning fox decided to dodge the lion and the bear. He seized the deer and ran off with it as fast as he could. The lion and the bear looked on helplessly. They said: 'How wise it would have been if we had shared the prey in a friendly way! Now, we have got nothing while the fox is enjoying a great meal.'

10. THE FOX AND THE TURTLE

A starving fox found nothing better to eat than a turtle once, but could not break through the solid shell for eating his prey. The shrewd turtle told the fox: 'If you put me in the water for some time, it'll soften me up.'

Taking the turtle at his word, the fox immersed it in the stream. Being a superb swimmer, the turtle soon swam to mid-stream. Safe at last, he raised his head and mocked at the fox: 'There are other animals who are more cunning than you. And now, you'll stay hungry.'

11. THE BEAR AND THE BEES

Once, a bear was wandering in search of food. He chanced to pass by a log where a swarm of bees had made their honey-comb. As the bear tried to sniff it, a bee stung him sharply. This made the bear lose his temper.

He swatted at the honey-comb with his paws. But this enraged the entire swarm of bees and they attacked him all over. The poor bear had to run to save himself.

12. THE SNAKE AND THE EAGLE

One day, a farmer, who was working in his field, saw an eagle trying to free itself from a snake's tight grasp. He hit the snake hard with a stick. The eagle flew to a branch of a tree, and the snake slinked away angrily. When the farmer returned home, the snake followed it to take its revenge. So did the eagle, out of curiosity.

As soon as the farmer entered his kitchen, he poured out water for himself, and went to wash his hands. The snake quickly went and spat its poison into the water, and slithered away. When the farmer lifted the glass of water, the eagle knocked it out of his hand, making the water fall down! Little did the farmer know that the eagle had saved his life, just as he had saved its life.

13. THE BLUEBIRD AND THE COYOTE

A long time ago, a coyote saw a bluebird, and asked him: 'How is that now you are blue and beautiful? I want to be blue, too.'

The bluebird taught the coyote a prayer, saying: 'Go and bathe in the lake four times each morning for four days and pray. The lake will turn your skin blue and beautiful.'

The coyote began to bathe and pray in the lake four times until he also became blue. Feeling proud, he ran around, but also kept turning around to see if his shadow had also turned blue! As he did so, once he banged into a tree so hard, that he fell down on the ground and became dust-coloured! And, to this day, all coyotes have the colour of the dusty earth.

14. THE STAG AND THE LION

A stag was once very proud of his magnificent antlers, but unhappy with his slim legs and hoofs. A lion began chasing him one day. The stag ran for his life but got stuck in a thicket. His antlers got stuck in the branches of a tree and he could not free himself. He was trapped!

Then, he realised that he had been foolish to discredit his legs and hoofs that helped him to run fast, while he had been unnecessarily proud of his huge antlers that had finally brought about his end.

15. THE CLEVER HARE

Long ago, there lived a cruel lion in a forest. He killed animals whether he was hungry or not. The animals held a meeting and decided to send one animal to the lion every day. A little later, it was the hare's turn. He thought the whole night of how he could save his life. The next day, he reached the lion's den very late. The lion was waiting impatiently, and asked him why he was so late. 'O King,' said the hare, 'I am so sorry. But, Your Majesty, I met another lion, who said he was the king, and wanted to eat me. I escaped with great difficulty.'

'Show me the villain,' roared the lion. The clever hare led him to a well filled with water. When he peeped inside and saw his reflection, the foolish lion thought it was the other lion. He roared angrily, jumped into the well and drowned! The hare rejoiced and returned to tell the other animals that they had nothing more to fear.

16. THE STORK IN THE HEN HOUSE

Once, a stork who had been flying on a long, migratory flight felt so tired, that it fell down. It crashed into a hen house, which also had a turkey and some ducks. The hens poked fun at the newcomer's ungainly, long legs. The stork ignored their insults and began talking about Africa, its hot desert and the ostriches there. The ducks did not understand anything and dismissed him off as a silly goose!

The turkey soon got bored and went away. Then, the hens and the ducks jumped on the stork, making such a noise that the farmer came by to see what had happened. As soon as he opened the door of the hen house, the stork flew away. The farmer felt sorry to see the stork go for if it had stayed, all the other farmers would have envied him. He angrily told the hens, "Don't think you are queens, for you will all be ending up in the stock pot!"

17. THE FLY AND THE ANT

One day, a fly and an ant got into a silly argument about who deserved the right of way. The fly said many horrible things. It taunted the ant, saying: 'You creepy, insignificant creature, I am the daughter of the air! How can you even think of comparing yourself to me? I go to palaces and homes of bishops, eating out of their plates. I even walk about on the king's crown!'

The ant heard the fly patiently, then said: 'I know that you land on heads, but it makes no difference to you whether it's the head of a king or the head of a donkey. Nobody welcomes you, least of all the palaces. Ants are tiny, but we wisely gather supplies for the winter to help us survive in the cold, dismal weather. I agree you can fly very high, but you fall to the ground with the first brush of cold weather. And even your wings cannot help you then!'

18. THE FOX AND THE ROOSTER

One evening, a rooster sat on a branch at the top of a tall tree, near the farm. He saw a fox, which was coming from the forest. The fox was searching for his dinner when he saw the plump rooster, and said: 'Hello, rooster! Come down and let's talk.'

'Don't think I'm so stupid that I'll believe you,' the rooster replied. The fox told the rooster that throughout the world, peace had been proclaimed between all animals. The rooster pretended to be very delighted and replied: 'In that case, it would be best to let that pack of hounds I can see from here, to reach you. Surely, they will show their brotherly affection for you!'

'But the dogs may not know of this wonderful news!' Saying this, the fox ran off as fast as his legs could carry him.

19. THE BIRDS AND THE MONKEYS

Once, there was a huge tree on the banks of a river. Some birds had built their nests on it, and lived there happily. One cold winter day, it began raining very heavily. Some monkeys who were playing nearby got drenched, and ran for shelter under the tree. All of them were shivering. The birds felt very sorry for the monkeys. They advised the monkeys to build a shelter for themselves.

At this, the monkeys got annoyed, thinking that the birds were making fun of them. When it stopped raining, the monkeys climbed up the tree and destroyed the birds' nests. The poor birds realised that they should not have given advice that was not asked for.

20. THE FOX WITH THE STUNTED TAIL

A fox had the bad luck of losing her tail in a trap and felt embarrassed. 'It's unfair,' she thought, 'why should I alone lack a tail?' She began to think that the world would be a much better place if no fox had a tail.

Cleverly, she tried to convince the other foxes to cut off their tails, saying: 'It is an extra burden. Nor can it be called elegant or pretty.' But one wise fox said: 'You are saying this out of a sense of shame. Had you not lost your tail, you would not have said this to us.' All the others laughed, and walked away, waving their bushy tails.

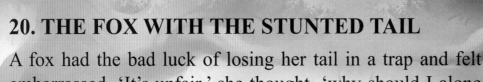

21. THE KING OF THE FOREST GOES TO WAR

The lion king was preparing to go to war and called all the other animals to get ready to do battle. His ministers advised him to leave the donkey and rabbit behind, as the first was very stupid and the second got very easily frightened.

The king overruled them: 'The donkey's voice is more resonant than mine, so he will be the trumpeter. While the rabbit will be an invaluable messenger, as he runs so fast.'

His advisers learnt that to win a war, the leader must be able to draw the best out of each one.

22. THE FOX AND THE GOAT

On a hot summer day, a thirsty fox was searching for water in a field. He came across a well with very little water in it. The clever fox saw that a pulley system was in place, which meant that one bucket would go down, bringing another bucket to the top. The fox quickly jumped into the bucket dangling at the top. Down went the bucket, and he gulped the water, quenching his thirst. But now he had to go up. A little later, a goat came along, looking for water, and peered into the well. The fox explained to the goat that if she wanted to drink water, she should get into the bucket at the top. When she came down, he would go up. 'But how will I get back?' she asked. 'Simple,' said the fox, 'I can come down, and you will go up.' Unaware of the cunning fox's plan, the goat agreed. Soon the fox was out, and went its way, leaving the poor goat in the well!

23. THE WOLF AND THE SHEPHERD

A cunning wolf began to follow a flock of sheep but did not attack them. As time passed, the shepherd lost his fear and thought of the wolf as a friend instead of an enemy.

One day, the shepherd visited the city for some work and left his flock in the wolf's care. When he returned in the evening, the poor shepherd found to his shock and dismay that each of his sheep had been killed by the wolf.

After thinking about this for long, he realised that it was entirely his fault, as he had been foolish enough to trust an enemy.

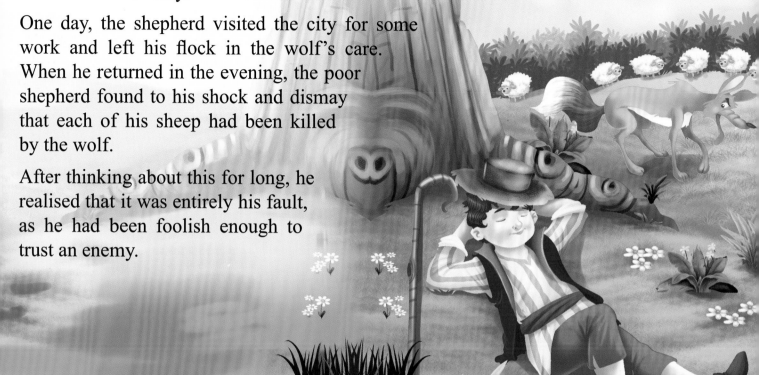

24. THE BELL ON THE CAT

Hundreds of years ago, the mice gathered to discuss their miserable condition. Each speaker blamed the horrible, wrongful cats for their plight, and they discussed ways of saving themselves.

Eventually, they came to a conclusion that met everyone's approval. A mouse suggested that a bell to be attached to every cat so that the mice would know whenever a cat was nearing, and go into hiding. This law is still valid! But, no mice ever came forward to offer to hang the bells around the cats' necks!

25. THE MARK OF WISDOM

An intelligent rabbit living in the African forests wanted to become wiser still and went to a witch for help. The witch told him to bring a living python to her. The clever rabbit cut off a long branch of a tree and took it to a python's lair. Showing it the branch, the rabbit asked the python to prove that it was longer than the branch. The python stretched itself along the branch. At once, the rabbit tied the snake to the branch and took it to the witch. She praised him but told him to next bring a swarm of bees to her.

The rabbit made a tiny hollow in a pumpkin, put some honey in the hole, and hung it near a beehive. When the bees entered the pumpkin to get the honey, the rabbit closed the hole and carried the bee-filled pumpkin to the witch.

Pleased, the witch rubbed a magic ointment in between the rabbit's ears, and a tiny white mark appeared. The African rabbits still bear this white spot, or their mark of wisdom!

26. THE CAMEL AND THE JACKAL

A camel and a jackal were friends. One day the camel carried the jackal on his back to a sugarcane field across the river. After having his fill, the jackal began to howl. The camel asked him not to do so, as it would bring the farmer there. 'It is my habit to sing after my meal,' replied the jackal.

The farmer heard the howls and ran towards his field. When he saw the camel eating sugarcanes, he drove it away with a good beating. The jackal ran through the bushes to meet his friend near the bank. And when they began to cross the river as before, the camel sat down in midstream. 'What are you doing?' said the jackal. 'It is my habit to take a bath after eating sugarcanes,' replied the camel. The jackal got drowned.

27. THE WOLF AND THE LAMB

A wolf saw a lamb drinking water from a stream, and searched for an excuse to attack and eat it. The wolf accused the lamb: 'Why are you dirtying my part of the stream?' Reasoned the little lamb: 'That's not possible; you are much more upstream, and the water does not flow up, it flows down!'

The wolf tried again: 'You're the same lamb who, last year, insulted my father.'

The lamb protested: 'I wasn't even born then!' The wolf growled: 'Enough of your nonsense! I shall not be denied this opportunity of eating you just because you're good at making excuses!'

28. THE FOX AND THE CROW

A crow was sitting grasping a piece of cheese in his beak. A fox saw him and made a cunning plan to get the cheese. He flattered the crow: 'You possess nearly everything, strength, beauty and wisdom. But, you need a beautiful voice to make you perfect.'

The vain crow wanted to prove to the fox that he had a melodious voice, and began to croak a song! Immediately, the cheese dropped from his beak, which the fox grabbed! Then, the fox mocked at the crow: 'Your biggest problem is that you are vain rather than being intelligent.'

29. THE FAITHFUL HORSE AND THE FOX

Once, a peasant had a horse that had served him for long, but on growing old, the horse could not gallop as fast as before. The master told the horse to leave and return only when he became strong like a lion! As the horse sadly trotted along down a road, he met his friend, a fox, and told her what had happened. The fox quickly thought up a plan. 'Quickly, lie on the road as if you were dead,' she told the horse, 'and see what I'll do!' Then, she ran to a lion's den. She told the huge lion that a horse was lying dead on the road and he could have a good meal. The lion wondered: 'How will I bring a big horse to my den?'

'I'll tie the horse to your tail,' said the cunning fox. Both ran to the road. She tied the horse to the lion's tail. Once the last knot was tightly tied, the fox exclaimed: 'Giddy up, boy! Off you go home!' The horse galloped home, dragging the furious lion behind, who struggled in vain to free himself, but got injured and died. At this strange sight, the peasant exclaimed: 'Old chap, you're even stronger than a lion! I'll never ask you to go now and take care of you always.'

30. THE LION AND HIS PARTNERS

The lion decided to form a company with the cow, the goat and the sheep. They decided to share everything equally. Once, they caught a deer and held a meeting to decide how to divide it amongst themselves. The lion insisted on making four equal parts.

He declared: 'As it's my right, the first share will be mine. Since I happen to be the King of the Forest, I will also take the second share, and since I am the strongest I will take the third share. If you claim the rest, I will also make mincemeat out of you!'

31. THE FOX AND THE MONKEY KING

In a forest, all the animals had collected to choose their new king. The monkey was chosen as he amused everyone with his antics. But, the fox was greatly disappointed for not being selected. He waited for an opportunity to take his revenge.

Finding a piece of meat lying on a path once, he immediately sensed that it had been set as bait. Pretending to be very loyal, he led the monkey king to the spot. The monkey fell for the bait and got trapped! The fox laughed aloud: 'When you have such little intelligence and can't save yourself, how will you rule and guide the other animals?'

32. THE ROOSTER, THE CAT AND THE MOUSE

A young, inexperienced mouse decided to see the world around him. First, he saw a rooster for the first time. He became so terrified of the rooster's pointed beak, its red crest, and feathers that he quickly scampered away. He next saw a cat from far, and admired its soft fur and brilliant eyes. Returning home that day, he told his mother all he had seen, who scolded him: 'You silly! Don't go by just what you see! That scary animal was actually a rooster that will never harm us, while the handsome animal is the cat, our biggest enemy!'

33. THE OWL AND THE SEAGULL

A seagull and an owl decided to work together. Having no money of its own, the owl borrowed a bit, while the seagull possessed a valuable jewel that it decided to invest. Both boarded a ship to go to a far-off place to begin their business. On the way, a storm struck the ship, which sank.

The seagull and owl escaped but lost their possessions. Since that time, the owl hides during the day from its creditors and only flies at night; while the seagull searches for its valuable jewel in the sea waters, as it flies over high rocks.

34. THE CAT AND THE OLD MOUSE

Wandering about, a black cat reached a warehouse where many mice lived. The cat lay on the ground, pretending to be dead. When the younger mice saw it, they shouted: 'A dead cat!' As they ran towards it, a wise old mouse stopped them, saying: 'Always remember, a cat has nine lives!'

The old mouse then climbed up a huge bin near the cat. A large sack of flour had been kept in this bin. The mouse chewed it open and the flour poured out all over the cat. It kept still for a moment, and, then, sneezed! The little mice saw that the cat was alive, only it had turned white!

35. THE CAT AND THE CROW

Once, a cat and a crow were good friends, and often spent time together. On a pleasantly sunny day, both were relaxing under a tree, when the crow saw a leopard moving towards them. At once, it flew into the high branches of a tall tree. The poor cat, with an injured foot, was left behind. It pleaded to its friend for help. The crow flew off, and soon came across some shepherds with their dogs. An idea came to it. It flew in front of the dogs, almost touching the ground, and then flew high in the direction of the leopard. The dogs followed the crow, bent on catching him. Hearing the dogs barking loudly, the leopard left the cat alone, and escaped into the jungle. And the crow saved his friend's life.

36. THE WEASELS AND THE MICE

War broke out between the weasels and the mice, in which the mice lost badly. The mice thought this had happened as they had no leaders. They were neither properly organised nor disciplined. The mice then selected some generals from amongst them, who made helmets for themselves with long horns, setting themselves apart from the others.

Even then, the mice were routed in the next battle and could save themselves only by rushing to hide in their burrows. But, the horned helmets of their generals prevented them from getting inside their burrows and they were eaten up by the weasels!

37. THE FOX AND THE GRAPES

A fox was starving and went looking for food to fill his empty stomach. Searching for a while, he reached a vineyard. Luscious grapes hanging from the vines high above tempted him. 'These must be delicious,' thought the fox and jumped up to grab the grapes, but could not reach them. He kept trying but failed each time.

Finally, he gave up, realising that the branches were far too high for him to reach. 'These grapes seem good but what if they're not ripe?' he consoled himself as he went away.

38. THE LION AND THE DONKEY

The lion decided to go hunting and chose the donkey for his companion, to use his distinctive braying effectively. Feeling very proud to be the lion's companion, the donkey stayed still as the lion draped a cloak of leaves around him. The stupid donkey thought it was a hunting costume, but it was a disguise. At the lion's command, the donkey went to a meadow and stood in the middle.

At a signal from the lion, he began braying loudly, terrifying the deer who tried to flee from this sudden, unknown attack. Rushing in all directions, a few landed in the lion's paws, while some landed in his jaws. The donkey claimed credit for the work done by him to make the hunt a successful one! The lion warned him immediately: 'Keep quiet, you silly donkey! Or, I might develop a taste for donkeys!' Wisely, the donkey fled, letting the lion take the entire credit for the hunt.

39. THE CUP WINNERS

It was the twelfth year when two animals were given a cup for being the fastest in the meadow. The hare won the first prize, but the second prize, given to the snail, stirred up a controversy. The sunflower, who was one of the judges, explained that strength and patience were considered while deciding the winners. The snail felt that he deserved the first prize. The lamp post told the snail: 'Each year, prizes are given in alphabetical order according to their Latin names. This, being the twelfth year, animals whose names begin with the letter L, such as Lepus the hare, and Lumachus the snail, were given the cups. The following year, animals whose names begin with M shall be considered.' The rose now spoke up: 'Actually, the sunbeam deserved the first prize. For when we are all gone and forgotten, she will still be shedding her radiance in this meadow!'

40. THE DOG AND THE DONKEY

Awakened by a sudden noise, a house dog woke up but immediately went off to sleep again. The donkey was astonished and asked: 'Shouldn't you be barking? These could be thieves!'

The dog replied: 'It would be better if you mind your own business.' Being rebuked like this, the donkey became angry and brayed as loudly as possible.

The thieves ran away and the master came running. He was so angry at being awakened for no reason, that he beat up the donkey badly. The experienced dog later told the donkey: 'Didn't I warn you? With a master like this, it's best to always think of yourself only.'

41. THE FOX AND THE WOLF IN COURT

The wolf once accused the fox of cheating him, while the fox said that the wolf had robbed him. They went to court, where the monkey was the judge. As the entire case was marked by contradictions, nobody could make any sense out of it, and the monkey lost all patience finally.

He ruled: 'I find the wolf to be guilty of having falsely accused the fox. The fox is also guilty, because, by his nature, he is a thief. Since the prison is the correct place for liars and robbers, I am sending you both to prison!'

42. THE SILLY WOLF AND THE BILLY GOAT

An old wolf was regarded as rather silly by the other wolves, for it was no longer so strong or clever as before. As it chased a billy goat, the goat leapt on a high rock. From its' safe perch, it said to the wolf: 'Why do you bother to chase me? If you open your mouth wide, I shall jump right inside!' As the silly wolf opened its mouth wide, the goat jumped...To land not inside its mouth but on its head, making such a strong landing that the wolf was knocked down. When the wolf came to his senses, with its mouth wide open, it could not remember whether it had eaten the billy goat or not!

43. THE HARE AND THE FROGS

A hare was annoyed with himself for not being brave and always running away from things. He made up his mind to be more courageous, but just then a sudden noise made him take to his legs!

He reached a pool, where all the frogs dived to hide inside its muddy waters, as soon as they heard the rabbit hopping along!

At once, the hare felt less angry with himself and thought: 'No matter how scared one is, there's always somebody else who feels more scared!'

44. THE MONKEY AND THE CROCODILE

Once, a monkey and a crocodile became friends. The monkey used to offer the crocodile sweet Jambolan fruits from the tree he lived on. One day, the crocodile took the fruits to his wife. After eating the sweet fruits, the greedy wife told her husband: 'Imagine how sweet that monkey's heart must taste, as he eats these sweet Jambolans every day!' She forced her husband to bring the monkey to their home.

The next day, the crocodile invited the monkey to his home for lunch. The monkey happily accepted the invitation and climbed onto the crocodile's back. On the way, the crocodile told the monkey that his wife was sick and had to eat a monkey's heart to save her life. The monkey understood the crocodile's evil intention. He quickly told the crocodile: 'Why didn't you tell me before? I've left my heart on the tree. Let us go back and bring it."

So, the foolish crocodile took the monkey back to the tree. The clever monkey climbed on to the tree and managed to save his life from his deceitful friend.

45. THE LION AND THE BADGER

A lion had become friends with a badger who lived alongside him. The lion trapped a sheep once and called out to his friend to join him for a meal. But, he got a rude answer: 'I have better things to attend to.' The next morning, the badger invited the lion to share some honey with him. But, the lion gave him the very answer that he'd got. On the third day, they met each other in the forest. As they chatted, they realised that neither of them had heard the invitation given by the other, and neither had given a rude reply!

They realised that someone was trying to create trouble between them. Hunting in the bushes near their dens for the culprit, they found a fox. Making it confess, the friends wanted to punish it. The cunning fox pleaded with them not to throw it into a pile of ashes nearby. This made the lion roar angrily. Together, the lion and the badger threw the fox onto that very pile of ashes. Upon this, the fox stirred up a huge cloud of dust and made off!

46. THE FOX AND THE STORK

To repay a debt, the fox once invited the stork over for dinner, though he did not really want to. Cunningly, he served a tasty soup in a shallow dish, which the stork's long beak could not manage to get hold of.

The stork did not complain but decided to teach the fox a lesson. She invited the fox to dinner. The stork cooked a delicious meal, serving it in a narrow, tall goblet so that the fox could not eat it, even his nose could not get into it!

47. THE DONKEY AND THE GRASSHOPPER

A donkey was unhappy with his voice. As he was grazing in a field one summer day, the pleasant sounds coming from the grasshoppers enthralled him. He asked one of them: 'What do you eat to make a delightful sound like that?'

The grasshopper jokingly told him it was dew, whereupon, the silly donkey decided to eat dew only. So, for the remainder of his life, he ate grass enthusiastically at dawn, as it was covered with dew. He earned a healthy appetite though his voice did not change.

48. THE MOUSE PRINCESS

Long ago, a queen gave birth to a daughter and the king held a big feast, but they forgot to invite the witch. The angry witch cast an evil spell on the infant, turning her into a mouse. She then said: 'The princess will turn into her real self, on the day on which my sister laughs.' All the clowns in his kingdom could not bring a smile to the face of the witch's sister, so the king ordered all cats to leave his kingdom, to save the royal mouse.

Years later, a neighbouring prince held a ball in his castle. The king's other three daughters went, leaving the mouse behind. But she tied a ribbon through a rooster's beak for her rein, and climbing its back, she also went. When the witch's sister saw this at the ball, she began to laugh! At once, the mouse changed into a lovely young lady, with whom the prince fell in love and married.

49. BONDO, THE WOLF, AND THE STRAY DOG

Becoming old, poor Bondo the wolf, always got into trouble. However, when he came across a skinny, stray dog with the bones showing, Bondo was delighted. He said loudly that he would eat the dog. The dog said: 'I'm too skinny, you will not relish me. Why don't you fatten me up first?'

Bondo liked the suggestion but by the time he had fattened the dog, the dog had gained enough strength to frighten the old wolf, by simply baring his teeth!

50. THE TWO ROOSTERS AND THE EAGLE

Two roosters lived together and fought often as both wanted to rule the farmyard roost. They agreed to fight a duel to decide who would be the ruler. Both fought valiantly.

Finally, however, one of them gave up and ran away. The winner proclaimed its victory by saying: 'Cock-a-doodle-doo', as it perched on a nearby wall.

Hearing the rooster cackle, an eagle swooped down and carried it away in its claws. And the loser became the winner!

51. THE MONKEYS AND THE BELL

A thief had stolen a bell and was running away with it when a tiger mauled him. Some monkeys found the bell and began ringing it. They made such a long, continuing din that the nearby villagers became fearful, thinking it might be a giant. But one woman was not scared. She took a basket of fruits to where she'd heard the bell ringing.

Setting down the fruit basket on the ground, she hid behind a bush. As soon as the monkeys pounced on the fruits, she picked up the bell and rushed back. The villagers praised her for her bravery in recovering the bell from a giant!

52. THE OX AND THE HORSE

A horse and an ox sensed that their master was about to go for a war. The horse worried about the dangers it would have to encounter during the battle. On the other hand, the ox was very cheerful as it knew that when the master was not there, it would have very little to do!

But the master's plan changed soon as news reached about the enemy having surrendered. In celebration of this victory, the cavalryman hosted a lavish banquet where roast meat was aplenty! Do you know who the loser was?

53. THE EAGLE AND THE BADGER

An eagle had made a nest for itself high up in an oak tree, while a badger lived in the tree's roots. Though they were not good friends, they kept out of each other's way. A cat went up to the eagle one day and told him: 'The badger is digging through the roots so that the tree falls and with it, your eaglets, which he will then eat!' She then climbed down and told the badger: 'Don't ever leave your home! That eagle above you is just waiting for you or your little ones to leave the house so that he can eat you all up.'

Both the eagle and the badger did not go to look for food for a few days. When their children were starving and facing death, they realised that they had been tricked. The infuriated eagle and badger then paid back the cat for her wickedness, by killing and eating her.

54. THE MONKEY AND THE DOLPHIN

One day, some sailors decided to go on a long voyage. One of them took his pet monkey with him. Suddenly, a terrible storm overtook their ship and everyone fell into the sea and got drowned. A dolphin that was passing by, saw the monkey drowning and picked him up. She thought that she would take him ashore on her back.

When they reached near an island, the dolphin asked the monkey: 'Do you know this place?' The monkey boasted: 'Yes. In fact, the king of this island and I are best friends!' The dolphin knew that no one lived on that island. She got angry and shook the monkey off her back for telling a lie.

55. THE SICK LION

The lion had severe indigestion so all the doctors in the forest went to see him. When the zebra irreverently remarked that His Majesty had bad breath, the furious lion killed him. The hyena, who had observed this, exclaimed over the pleasant smell all around. The lion said that he was not stupid and killed him also.

Lastly, the lion turned to the cunning fox for his opinion. The fox saved his skin by craftily saying that his nose was blocked due to a cold, and he could not smell a thing!

56. THE SNAKE AND THE ANTS

Long ago, there lived a poisonous snake in a hole. All the small creatures living around his hole were afraid of him. This had made him very proud and he thought himself to be the most powerful creature.

One day, the snake saw an ant-hill near the hole where he lived. The arrogant snake thought: 'Why should there be an ugly ant-hill near my hole?' He tried to break the ant-hill.

But within a minute, thousands of ants came out and attacked the snake, biting his body all over. The snake could not bear the pain and died in no time.

57. THE WOLF AND THE GOAT

A small goat had gone to pasture with his flock. Snow had covered most of the grass growing there. It was bitingly cold and very windy. The goat found a sheltered hollow, and soon fell asleep. Awakening, he found his flock had gone back to their fold, and he would have to find his way home alone. Unluckily, he met a wolf who offered to walk him home. The goat said that he could manage by himself.

The wolf said that he was worried that the goat might be gobbled by a wicked animal. The goat sadly observed that he did not think anybody else would eat him, except the wolf! At that, the wolf remarked that rather than the goat be eaten up by someone else, he would devour him instead! And springing on the goat, he made mincemeat of him.

58. THE PEACOCK AND THE CRANE

The peacock often made fun of the crane, telling it that it looked very drab. The vain peacock boasted that its feathers were draped in gold and purple, while the crane had very unbecoming wings.

The crane retorted that it could sing to the stars as it flew high in the sky, but the peacock had to drag itself on the ground, as lowly chickens did in their farmyard.

59. THE PIGEON AND THE ANT

Long ago, on the bank of a lake stood a tree with a pigeon's nest. At the bottom of the tree lived an ant. Both were good friends. One day, the ant suddenly slipped into the lake. The pigeon saw this. Immediately, he tore off a leaf from the tree's branch and dropped it near the ant. She quickly got onto the leaf. The pigeon grabbed the leaf in his claws and flew safely to the land with the ant.

A few days later, the pigeon was sitting on the tree when a hunter came there. Seeing the pigeon, he aimed an arrow at him. The ant had seen the hunter. It quickly climbed up his leg and bit him hard. The hunter yelled and missed his aim. Hearing the scream, the pigeon quickly flew away.

60. THE DONKEY WHO SANG A SONG

Once, a donkey and a jackal were wandering at night, and spotted a field full of juicy tomatoes. Going inside, they ate the red juicy tomatoes to their heart's content. The donkey was very happy and said: 'I feel like singing.'

The jackal warned him: 'Please, don't make any noise. The owner of the field will hear you and will come running with sticks.'

But the donkey did not pay any attention to the jackal's advice, and began to bray loudly. Realising the danger that would come, the jackal left the field and hid behind a nearby tree. Hearing the loud braying, the owner of the field ran to the spot with a heavy stick in his hand. He beat the donkey so hard that the donkey forgot to sing and cried in pain.

61. THE DECEITFUL CRANE

There once lived an old crane on the banks of a lake. Being unable to hunt, he hatched an evil plan. One day, he sat sadly on a rock on the lake's bank. The other water creatures asked him why he was so sad. He replied: 'I have heard that this lake is going to be filled up with mud.'

All the creatures were very worried. The crane said: 'I can carry you to another lake far away.' The creatures thanked him. The wicked crane started taking away one fish each day. On the way, he would dash it to the rocks and eat it up. One day, a crab requested to be taken. A little later, when he saw piles of fish bones on the rocks below, he guessed the truth.

He said: 'Uncle Crane, may I sit on your neck for sometime?' The crane let him do so. The crab drove his claws into the crane's neck, and killed him. On returning to the lake, he told everyone about the crane's wickedness.

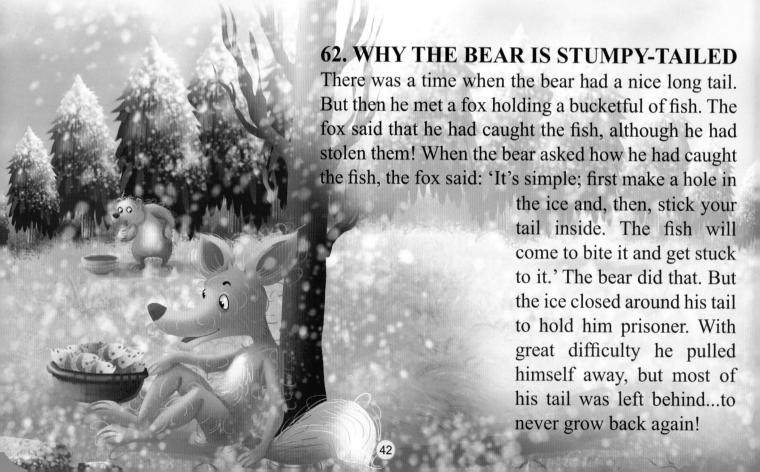

62. WHY THE BEAR IS STUMPY-TAILED

There was a time when the bear had a nice long tail. But then he met a fox holding a bucketful of fish. The fox said that he had caught the fish, although he had stolen them! When the bear asked how he had caught the fish, the fox said: 'It's simple; first make a hole in the ice and, then, stick your tail inside. The fish will come to bite it and get stuck to it.' The bear did that. But the ice closed around his tail to hold him prisoner. With great difficulty he pulled himself away, but most of his tail was left behind...to never grow back again!

63. THE GOAT AND THE DONKEY

A village washer-man owned a donkey to carry loads of clothes, and a goat that gave milk. The master fed his goat a good diet, but kept her tied up at home the whole day. This made her very jealous of the donkey that used to go to the river each day and enjoy nature's beauty. Cunningly, she once sympathised with the donkey for the hard work he did. She told him to pretend he had broken his leg, so that he would get some rest. The stupid donkey agreed, but he actually broke his leg! The doctor told the master that the donkey should be fed goat soup. The kind master decided to save his donkey, by killing his goat. As he approached her with a knife, the goat regretted her ill-advice and ran for her life.

64. THE LION AND THE GRATEFUL MOUSE

A hungry lion caught a small mouse one day. Just as he was about to eat it, the mouse begged: 'Please set me free and I will help you one day.'

The lion king roared with laughter at this absurdity, but let the mouse go. Some days later, the lion got trapped in a net that had been set by hunters. As the lion lay there feeling miserable, the grateful mouse came and nibbled through the net, setting the lion free. 'Now you know how even the weak can help the mighty,' the mouse told the lion.

65. THE CROW AND THE SWAN

One day, a crow saw a swan swimming in a pond. The crow was very pleased to see the sparkling white colour of the swan. He asked the swan: 'You look so beautiful. What is the secret of your beauty and white feathers?'

The swan replied: 'I am white and beautiful because I live in water all the time. You will also become white if you stay in the water like me.'

Hearing this, the crow jumped into the pond. But only in a few minutes, he felt as if his body was going to freeze. With utmost difficulty, he managed to come out of the pond. He was shivering all over with cold and still as black as ever!

The swan was amused. So he mocked at him: 'Are you afraid of water? What about your whim to be white? I never imagined that you would give up so soon.'

The crow had no reply to give. He thought to himself: 'Crows are not meant to live in water. I was a fool to have even tried to do so.'

66. THE WICKED SNAKE

Once upon a time, there lived a pair of crows on a huge tree. They lived happily till a big snake made its home at the bottom of that tree. Whenever the crows went in search of food, the snake crawled up the tree and ate up all their eggs. The crows became very sad, and thought of a plan to teach the evil snake a lesson.

And the next morning, the female crow picked up a necklace of a princess while she was bathing and flew away. Seeing this, the royal guards chased the crow. The crow dropped the necklace into the snake's hole and it came slithering out.

When the guards saw the snake, they took out their spears and killed it. Then they safely took the necklace out of the hole and went back to the princess. The crows were very happy that their plan had worked, and they lived happily on the same tree.

67. THE ELEPHANT AND THE DOG

Long ago, a royal elephant was very well fed and well-groomed. In his neighbourhood was a stray dog. He visited the elephant's shed, and fed on the leftovers. The elephant was usually alone, and liked the dog's company. They became good friends. The dog became healthy. A farmer visited the mahout once. He wanted to buy the dog, and the mahout gave it to him. The elephant began to pine for his friend, and stopped eating and drinking. The king sent his wisest minister to look into the matter. When questioned, the mahout admitted that the elephant had been very friendly with a dog, which had been taken by someone. The king announced that whoever had taken the dog should release him, or face a heavy fine. Immediately, the farmer released the dog. The elephant was overjoyed to be re-united with his friend, and they both lived happily after that.

68. THE SICK CAMEL

A camel who lived near the edge of an oasis fell sick. When his relatives and friends learnt that he was alone and sick, they came to visit him. After journeying for long, they rested for awhile, staying back with the sick camel, and took to eating the grass growing around. The camel felt very happy to meet his relatives and friends. But, when he had recovered and looked around for something to eat, he found that everything had been eaten up by his visitors! So, the camel had no choice but to trudge on through the desert, to search for another oasis.

69. THE OWL AND THE NIGHTINGALE

A nightingale was kept caged near a window once. The nightingale was in the habit of singing only at night. An owl was very confused by this and asked the nightingale the reason for his behaviour.

The nightingale told him: 'When I was trapped, it was day and I was singing. I realised that I should be more prudent and began singing only at night.'

'Do you fear you may be captured again?' asked the owl, plainly baffled. 'I think it would have been better for you if you had been more careful the first time, when your freedom was at risk. It shouldn't matter anymore to you, now.'

70. TRUE, VERY TRUE

A greatly respected hen broke off one of her feathers one day, with her beak. She sighed deeply: 'I've broken another feather! I'll never look beautiful!' Her neighbour told the mother hen: 'One of my sisters is trying to make herself look beautiful by pulling out all her feathers.'

The owl, sitting atop the hen house remarked: 'Shameless creature!' His wife admonished him, saying: 'Quiet! The children should not hear this.'

But she herself flew off and told the pigeons: 'Did you know? One of the hens is in love with the rooster and has plucked out all her feathers!'

The pigeons related this story but it was about two featherless hens! When it reached back to the hens, they learnt that five or six hens had lost their feathers after fighting over the rooster! The first hen, who had no idea that this had started because of her, exclaimed: 'What a scandal! These hens should be ashamed of themselves.'

71. THE TWO GOATS

There lived two wise goats in a village. They never quarrelled with each other. All the other animals were jealous, and wanted to see them fight. The goats were aware of this. There was a narrow bridge over a river in the village. Only one creature could pass over it at one time. One day, the jealous animals urged one goat to graze on one side of the river, and sent the other goat to the other side. At sunset, one of the goats began to cross the river. Seeing this, the animals sent the other goat onto the bridge from the other side. The animals were sure that the goats would lock horns! But the goats didn't fight. One of them lay down while the other leapt over her carefully. The other animals were disappointed, but had to praise the goats' wisdom.

72. THE BEES AND THE HORNETS GO TO COURT

Once, the bees and the hornets had a serious dispute, as both laid claim to the honey in a honeycomb. To settle the matter, they landed up in the court. The judge, who was a wasp, could not decide who were the rightful owners. Witnesses testified that black and yellow insects had been seen going in and out of the honeycomb, but this did not help, as both bees and hornets have black and yellow bodies!

The Queen Bee lost her patience. She told the judge: 'Why don't you let the bees and hornets make another honeycomb? Whichever group builds the best comb in the shortest time, can be declared the owner of that comb.' As the hornets cannot build honeycombs, they refused to accept this proposal. And the wasp understood that the honey and honeycomb could only rightfully belong to the bees!

73. THE FAR-SIGHTED SWAN

Long ago, a group of swans had made their nests among the branches of a huge tree. One day, an old, wise swan saw a smaller twiner growing near the tree. He warned the others: 'This twiner may bring danger for us in future.' But nobody paid any attention. After a few days, a bird-catcher came to that tree, and climbed up by means of the same twiner. He set a net to catch the swans and came down. As soon as the swans flew to their nests, they got entrapped in their nests.

They all cried for help. Then, the wise swan made a plan. When the bird-catcher came, he found them lying motionless. Taking them to be dead, he dropped them on to the ground. To his surprise, they all flew away at once!

74. THE HARE AND THE TORTOISE

Once there was a speedy hare, who bragged about how fast he could run, and mocked at the slow pace of the tortoise. One day, he challenged the tortoise to a race. Tired of hearing him boast, the tortoise agreed. On the day of the race, all the animals gathered to watch. At the start signal, the hare was off to a quick start, leaving the tortoise far behind.

Seeing that the tortoise was nowhere around, the hare thought of resting awhile. Soon he fell fast asleep. Meanwhile, the tortoise had been slowly and steadily plodding along, and reached the finishing line. The animals who were watching, cheered so loudly that the hare woke up. He began to run again. When he saw that the slow tortoise had won, the proud hare hung his head in shame.

75. THE ANT AND THE GRASSHOPPER

One fine morning, a grasshopper lay happily on a leaf, playing his violin. An ant came by, carrying grains of corn to its nest. He greeted her with a broad smile: 'Why are you working so hard on such a lovely day? Come, sit with me and sing a song.'

The ant refused, saying: 'I am storing up food for the winter.' The grasshopper said: 'There is plenty of time for that!' But the ant quietly went on its way.

After a few months, winter set in. The grasshopper had not stored any food. Dying of hunger, he went to the ant and begged for some food. She smiled and said: 'You kept laughing at me when I was working! You sang during the whole summer. You can now dance the winter away!'

76. THE SWAN AND THE GOOSE

On the same day once, a swan and a goose were bought by the same buyer. He took them to his villa and put them in his lake, as the swan was easy on the eyes, while the goose would eventually become plump and make for a sumptuous meal.

The two birds became friends and swam about happily in the lake. Their master and his guests often came by to admire them and fed them tasty tidbits. Finally, the master told the cook to serve the goose's roasted meat to him at dinner time.

The cook went to do his master's bidding. But being very drunk, he seized the swan instead! When he was about to cut the swan's throat, the swan broke out into a song! The astonished cook abandoned the idea of killing the bird.

77. THE MUSICIANS OF BREMEN

A hard-working donkey who had run away from a cruel master met an old dog who had been thrown out. They began to travel together. As the donkey could bray and the dog could bark, they planned to go to the city of Bremen to sing in the choir! They were joined by a cat and a rooster. At night, they found a well-lit hut in the forest.

Four fearsome bandits lived here. The animals peeped in and saw a delicious meal, and planned to get it. The dog climbed on top of the donkey, the cat climbed on the dog, and the rooster went right to the top. Together they screamed. Thinking it was a terrible monster, the bandits fled! Happily, the four animals rushed inside and ate up all the food!

78. REYNARD THE FOX AND THE FISHES

After a day by the river, a fisherman returned home with a cartful of fishes. Reynard, the fox, saw him and plotted a way of getting a rich meal. Lying down in the centre of the road, he pretended to be dead.

On seeing the limp fox, the fisherman fell for the trick. Thinking that he could use the beautiful fox skin, he lifted the fox and put him in the back of his cart. As soon as they moved, Reynard released all the fishes into the road behind him, and then, picked them up and ran off! The poor, gullible fisherman lost not only the fox skin, but also his fishes.

79. THE THIRSTY CROW

It was a hot summer day. A crow felt very thirsty and flew about hither and thither in search of water. He got very tired and came to a tree. Suddenly the crow caught sight of a pitcher which had a little water in it.

The crow looked about carefully and saw some pebbles lying near the pitcher. At once, he hit upon an idea. Picking up the pebbles one by one, he dropped them into the pitcher. Soon the water in the pitcher came up. The crow quenched his thirst and flew away.

80. THE ROOSTER AND THE JEWEL

Once, there lived a rooster near a farmyard. One day, while searching for food for himself and his hens, he scratched the ground with his claws. He dug and finally found something hard. 'Cock-a-doodle-do!' cried the rooster, 'that's for me,' and soon rooted it out from beneath the ground.

But the moment the rooster picked it up, he was amazed to find a beautiful jewel. He did not know what to do with it. He said: 'It looks very fine. It may be very precious to some people but I would rather have found one grain of corn.'

81. THE VIPER, THE FROGS AND THE WATER SNAKE

Often a viper drank water from a pond that a water snake said was his. They both decided to settle the matter, once and for all, by a fight. The frogs who were the perennial enemies of the water snake, lent their support to the viper.

When the day of the contest dawned, the frogs began croaking, as they couldn't think of anything else to do. The viper won. Later, when the frogs asked the viper for their share, the viper began whistling, leaving the frogs baffled. The viper told them: 'I'm repaying you in the same manner by which you helped me!'

82. THE LARKS IN THE CORN FIELD

A family of larks lived in a nest in a corn field. Each day, as the mother lark went to search for food, she told the little larks to stay inside the nest and beware of the farmer. One day, the little larks heard the farmer telling his son: 'The corn is ready to be cut. We must call our neighbours to help us to reap this field.'

The little larks got frightened. When their mother returned in the evening, they told her what the farmer had said. The mother lark smiled and said: 'Don't be afraid.' The next day, the farmer again came to the field and said: 'We will have to call our relatives to reap this field.' The little larks again got scared, but their mother again told them not to fear.

The third evening, when the mother lark came home, the little larks said: 'Mother! The farmer came again. He said that he would reap this field tomorrow.'

Hearing this, she said: 'My dear children, now we must leave this field tomorrow before the farmer arrives. When a man says he will do his job himself, he will surely do it.'

83. THE BOAR AND THE FOXES

A wild boar stood under a tree one day. He was rubbing his tusks against the trunk of the tree to sharpen them. After some time, two foxes came there and watched the wild boar sharpening his tusks. Feeling amused, one of them asked him: 'Why are you doing that? There is neither any hunter, nor any other danger in sight.'

'True,' replied the boar, 'but whenever a danger appears, I won't get any time to sharpen my teeth. I have to keep them ready for use all the time. Only then I can stay safe in this forest.'

84. THE FARM ROOSTER AND THE WEATHERVANE

Once upon a time, there were two roosters. One was fixed to the roof of a farmhouse. It showed which way the wind was blowing. The other one lived at the farm happily.

He was proud of his red crest and his 'Cock-a-doodle-doo'.

One day the weather became very bad. The farm rooster ran for shelter, but the weathervane proudly stood in its place. As night fell, the wind became too harsh and it blew down the weathervane. In the morning, when the storm had passed over, the farm rooster crowed: 'Cock-a-doodle-doo'. But the weathervane lay useless on the ground.

85. HOW THE GREEDY FOX MET ITS END

One day, a hunter spotted a big, fat donkey in a forest. He set an arrow to his bow and aimed it at the donkey, injuring it seriously. But when the hunter went near the donkey, it kicked him so hard that he died then and there. As the donkey had been injured very severely, it also died after some time. A greedy fox was seeing all this from behind a bush. He was thrilled: 'Today is my lucky day, indeed! I will feed on a donkey and a man!'

The fox went to the donkey and decided to eat the flesh from its wound. As soon as he dug his teeth into the flesh, the sharp tip of the arrow that was inside the donkey's body, pierced his palate. As a result, the fox too met with its end.

86. THE TWO MULES AND THE ROBBERS

Two mules were trudging along the same path. One was owned by a miller and was carrying oats. The other worked for a banker and was loaded with a chest of gold coins.

Proudly it trotted along on its path, but hearing the sounds of the clinking coins, some robbers guessed what it was carrying.

Not only did they steal the treasure, but also rained sticks on the poor animal.

The first mule smirked: 'Being important and rich certainly has some disadvantages!'

87. THE GOLDEN BIRD

Once upon a time, a king got a large tank built in his palace garden, in which he kept beautiful swans. These swans had gorgeous feathers and they were very proud of their beauty. One day, a beautiful bird with a golden body flew in and perched near the tank. When the king saw this bird, he asked it to stay in the garden forever. He named it the golden bird. Every morning, the king fed tasty grains to the golden bird with his own hand.

The swans became jealous of the golden bird. They thought that the king did not love them as before. So, they started attacking the golden bird. They also asked it to leave, but the golden bird refused. The enraged swans started cackling aloud in anger. It disturbed the king and everyone else in the palace.

Suspecting rightly what had caused this commotion, the king ordered his soldiers to kill all the swans. When the swans saw the soldiers marching towards them with arrows and spears, one of them said that they should all fly away. And all of them lost their royal home because of their jealousy.

88. THE DONKEY IN THE TIGER'S SKIN

There lived a washerman who had a donkey. He used the donkey to carry clothes to his clients. The donkey was tired of carrying clothes here and there. One day, while grazing in the forest, the donkey found a tiger's skin. He thought: 'If I wear this skin, I shall look like a tiger.' Wearing it, he moved proudly towards a village.

Wherever the donkey went, the other animals and people mistook him for a tiger and were afraid of him. The donkey felt so proud and happy, that he began to bray loudly. The people heard him braying and realised that he was not a tiger. They chased him with sticks in their hands, and the poor donkey had to run away to save his life.

89. THE CROWS' CHALLENGE

Long ago, two crows were good friends. Once, they got into an argument and challenged each other to a contest, to see which one could fly higher while carrying a sack.

One crow filled cotton into his sack and was amused to see the other crow filling his sack with salt, which was heavier. Then, both took flight.

The crow with light cotton in his sack flew higher than the other one. But soon, it began to rain. The cotton soaked up the raindrops and grew heavy! It became hard for him to fly.

On the other hand, the salt in the second crow's sack dissolved in the rain, and his sack became very light! Now, he flew up higher and won the challenge!

90. THE EAGLE AND THE WOODCUTTER

One day, a woodcutter saw an eagle that had been caught in a trap. Being kind-hearted by nature, he set the eagle free. The eagle looked at the woodcutter in gratitude and flew away.

Some time later, the woodcutter thought of having his lunch, and sat down on a rock atop a hill. Just then, the eagle flew down and took away the woodcutter's hat. He got up and ran after the eagle. As soon as he moved away from the rock, it gave way with a crash! As a result, the woodcutter escaped being hurt. The grateful eagle had repaid its well-wisher.

91. THE BIRDCHILD AND THE WITCH

During his round of inspection once, a gamekeeper, who was also a wizard, found a newborn child, which had been stolen by an eagle from its cradle. The wizard took the baby, Birdchild, home and brought it up alongside his daughter, Lena. The eagle was actually a witch in disguise, who wanted to eat the boy. She began working as a housekeeper in the wizard's home as an old woman.

Lena discovered the witch's plan and fled with Birdchild. The witch changed into an eagle and followed. Lena changed Birdchild into a pool of water and herself into a duck. The witch recognised Birdchild and bent to gulp water. Lena grabbed the eagle and made it drown. And the two children returned home safely.

92. THE GREEDY DOG

A dog was running off one day, with a huge chunk of meat he had stolen, holding it tightly in his jaws. On reaching the river's bank, he looked into the water and saw another dog holding a huge piece of meat in its jaws, just as big as his! He did not know that he was seeing his own reflection and jumped into the water to steal the other dog's meat. But when he fell into the water, he had to let go of the meat in his mouth, to save himself from drowning. And finally, he had nothing left to eat!

93. THE LITTLE GOLDFISH

Fishing in the sea, a poor fisherman once found a little goldfish in his net. The tiny fish waved its fins frantically, moving its mouth as if begging him to let it go. Taking pity, he threw it back into the sea, though he knew he could have sold it to a goldsmith and earned a lot of money.

'I will reward you for your kindness, but don't say anything to anybody,' the goldfish said.

Returning home, the fisherman found that his miserable hut had become a grand castle and his wife was wearing an expensive gown. 'How have we become so rich?' she asked, giving no peace to her poor husband until he had told her about the goldfish. As he spoke, the castle became their old hut! Again they were poor and his wife became dissatisfied.

94. THE EAGLE AND THE CROW

There lived a crow on a tree top. Every day he used to watch with utter wonder the acts of an eagle. The eagle had a nest high up on a mountain. One day, the crow saw the eagle swoop down on a lamb. He clutched it in its claws and carried it to his nest. The crow was amazed. His silly head was filled with the idea: 'If the eagle can perform this feat, why can't I?'

And up he flew as high as he could. From there he tried to swoop down and catch a lamb. But, instead he dashed against the ground. His head and beak cracked. A bird-catcher saw the fluttering crow and at once guessed what had happened. Running up, he caught the bird and locked him in a cage. So, the black crow that tried to mimic the black eagle, was laughed at by everybody.

95. THE FOX AND THE LEOPARD

One day, a fox and a leopard had a dispute over which of the two was more beautiful. The leopard was very proud of his glossy spots. He made insulting remarks about the fox. But the wise fox who prided himself on his bushy tail, kept quiet. This enraged the leopard and he was about to lose his temper.

The fox remarked: 'You may have glossy spots, but my beauty is not external. I have a sharp mind that makes me more attractive than you.'

96. THE HUNTER AND THE RABBIT

A hunter once caught a rabbit and was carrying it home for his evening meal.

The clever rabbit thought of a plan to save itself. It said to the hunter: 'If you let me go, I'll show you where the rest of my companions are hiding. Thus, you will have a larger catch.'

The hunter was very wise indeed. He said to the rabbit: 'You cannot take me in with your oily tongue. If you can betray your friends, how can you do me any good? So, for betraying your friends, you must die.'

Saying this, the hunter killed the rabbit.

97. THE THIRSTY ANT

One day, an ant desperately scurried around in search of water. It was on the verge of death, when a drop of water landed near its mouth, and saved it! It was a tear actually, containing all the qualities that flow out of suffering. The ant found that it was now able to understand and speak the human language! Visiting a grain store one day, the ant found a little girl, sitting on the floor and crying. When the ant asked her why she was crying, she said that she had been imprisoned by an ogre. He had told her to make three heaps of grain, rye and barley out of huge mounds of seeds all mixed together. She said that if she did not finish the task by the next dawn, the ogre would have her for his supper!

The ant cheered her up. He fetched all his friends, and they set to work. The next day, the ogre found the three mounds he'd wanted! So, the little girl's tear came to her rescue!

98. THE HEN WITH SILVER EGGS

One day, a woman went to the market and bought a beautiful hen. A few days later, to her great surprise, the hen laid a silver egg!

The woman became very greedy. She thought that if the hen laid more than one egg each day, she would never have to work. So, she made her hen eat more and more, to make it lay more eggs.

The next morning, she hoped that the hen would have laid more than one egg. But she was shocked to find that her hen was dead! The hen died of overeating, and she lost even the single egg it used to lay.

99. THE HUNTING DOG AND THE GUARD DOG

A man had two dogs. He trained one dog to hunt and the other to be a guard dog.

But, even though the hunting dog fetched game for his master, it was the guard dog who got the tastiest morsels!

The hunting dog was annoyed. He protested to the guard dog one day: 'This is unfair. I hunt all day long, while you get your food without doing any work.'

The guard dog replied: 'That's up to the master. He feels it's more important to reward the protector of his home, than the one that goes hunting with him.'

100. THE SPARROWS AND THE ELEPHANT

Long ago, a sparrow couple made a nest on a branch of a banyan tree. One day, a mighty elephant pulled down a branch of the tree that had their nest. Their eggs broke. The sparrow couple cried bitterly and went to seek help from their friends. The crow couple, the frog, and the flies, made a plan to teach the elephant a lesson.

The next day, the flies flew near its' ears, making a buzzing sound. The crow couple immediately swooped down and pecked the elephant in both the eyes, making him blind. Just then, the frog croaked. Thinking he was close to a pond, the elephant went in that direction, but fell into a deep ditch and died.

101. FELIX THE TERRIBLE AND THE FOX

On meeting a cat in the forest, the fox learnt it was Felix the Terrible, and he was the king's new governor. The fox thought that if she was seen in the governor's company, it would add to her prestige. After sometime, they got married and began living in a woodcutter's hut.

The fox spread the news that the new governor, her husband, was very ferocious. To befriend him, the bear took an ox for him, while the wolf took a sheep. Being scared, they sent a hare to inform the governor first. The bear hid in a tree and the wolf took refuge in a hole. The cat attacked the meat noisily. Just then, the wolf shifted and the leaves rustled. The startled cat jumped into the air, landing on the wolf's nose! The terrified wolf sprang up and ran away! And all forest animals have been fearful of cats since then.